# GRANDMA'S

## BOOK OF AMAZING, WEIRD AND WACKY SCIENCE TRICKS AND FACTS TO EXPLORE WITH YOUR GRANDKIDS

You know you're a cool grandma. Your grandkids might know it too. But being cool has responsibilities. It's up to you to keep your grandkids entertained and show them just how wacky, wise, and wonderful you are! This book can help.

We've gathered the weirdest facts, tricks, and experiments for you to share with your grandkids. This book contains it all, from freaky human body tricks to amazing recipes, crazy nature facts, magic tricks, math marvels, and science experiments that are easy to do at home. We've also assembled lots of weird and wonderful facts about the human body and a few other topics that will amaze and astound kids of all ages. These tricks and facts will help you create good times and memories that your family will cherish for a lifetime.

So sit back, relax, and check out all the crazy cool activities in this book. After you've tried them, there will be absolutely no doubt that you are the coolest and most fun grandma in the neighborhood!

These projects are recommended for children 8 and above. Grandparents, always carefully supervise your grandchildren when enjoying these activities together, especially around water, in the kitchen, or when using sharp objects. Remember that any activity involving small parts can present a choking hazard and is not suitable for children under the age of 3. Before beginning any activity, take into consideration your grandchildren's ages, abilities, and any allergies they may have, and adapt your plans accordingly. Stay safe and have fun!

Grandma's Book of Amazing, Weird and Wacky Science Tricks and Facts to Explore with Your Grandkids
ISBN 978-1-7325781-5-9
Published by Product Concept Mfg., Inc., 2175 N. Academy Circle #201, Colorado Springs, CO 80909
©2019 Product Concept Mfg., Inc.  All rights reserved.
Written and Compiled by Joanne Mattern in association with Product Concept Mfg., Inc.

# CHAPTER 1: CRAZY HUMAN BODY TRICKS

*We often take our bodies for granted. It seems pretty ordinary to be able to stand up and move around. But our bodies are home to some pretty freaky tricks! Check out the ideas below and find out the science behind some amazing human tricks!*

# OFF CENTER TRICKS

Here's something really weird. Bend over and hold your toes. Try to jump forward. You can't do it! But you will have no trouble jumping backward. Why? It all has to do with balance and gravity.

To keep your balance, you have to keep your center of gravity (which is usually around your belly button) over your feet. If you can't do that, you'll fall. When you move, your center of gravity shifts slightly to keep you in balance. Changing your body's shape shifts your center of gravity.

The reason you can't jump forward while bent over and holding your toes is that your body wants to shift your center of gravity forward. But it can't do that because your fingers are holding your toes and preventing you from shifting your balance onto them. However, jumping backward is no problem because nothing is preventing your center of gravity from shifting onto your heels.

Here are some more weird tricks that work because your center of gravity can't rebalance your body.

Sit in a chair with your back against the chair and your feet on the floor. Try to stand up while keeping your back straight. You can't do it! When you are sitting, your center of gravity is at your waist, which is supported by the chair. When you try to stand up with your back straight, your center of gravity can't move to your new support base, which is above your feet, so you are glued to your chair!

Stand with your right side pressed against a wall. Try to move your left leg without moving sideways. You can't, because the wall prevents you from shifting your center of gravity over your right foot.

Stand with your back straight against the wall. Then try to bend over and pick up an object on the floor in front of you without moving your feet. Did you almost fall over? That's because when you stand straight against the wall, your center of gravity is over your feet. When you bend forward, your center of gravity shifts forward. In order to keep your balance, you must move your feet forward to keep your balance. Since the rules of this challenge do not allow you to move your feet, and the wall prevents you from shifting your center of gravity backward, you will fall flat on your face.

# THE FLOATING ARM TRICK

This trick makes you feel like you don't have any control over your own body! Press the backs of your hands against the inside of a door frame for 30 seconds, as if you're trying to make the frame wider. Then let your arms down. Your arms will float up from your sides, as if lifted by an external force. Scientists call this Kohnstamm phenomenon. It happens because your brain and the nerve cells in your arms get mixed up. Moving your arms up is an involuntary movement, but holding your arms down is a voluntary movement. The brain gets both signals at once, and reacts by going with the involuntary move to lift your arms.

# BRAINY HAND TRICKS

Stick out both index fingers as if you are pointing at something. Slowly begin rotating them in the same direction. Do this slowly at first, then gradually increase the speed. As your fingers rotate faster, something weird happens. They are now moving in opposite directions, and it's almost impossible to keep them moving in the same direction. Usually the dominant hand will set the pace and direction. The less-dominant hand will not be able to keep up and will start to move in a different direction. Or it will jerk back and forth.

With a lot of practice and concentration, you can overcome this response and make both fingers move in the same direction. However, this trick shows that our brains are hard-wired in very specific ways, and it is very difficult to change that.

# CONFUSING LEGS

Here's another trick that will make you feel challenged. Lift your right foot a few inches from the floor and begin to move it in a clockwise direction. While you're doing this, use your right index finger to draw a number 6 in the air. Your foot will turn in an counter-clockwise direction and there's nothing you can do about it!

This effect happens because the left side of your brain, which controls the right side of your body, is responsible for rhythm and timing. The left side of your brain cannot deal with operating two opposite movements at the same time and so it combines them into a single motion. In fact, if you try this trick with your left foot and right hand you should have no problem!

Another reason is that the nerve cells controlling the movement of your arm also control the movement of your leg. If you try to do two things at once, your nerve cells have to fight it out. Whichever cells win control the direction. Usually, the arm has the more dominant nerve cells, so that movement controls the leg as well.

# JUMPING FINGER

Hold your finger in front of your nose. Close your left eye. Now open your left eye and close your right eye. What happens? Your finger jumps without you moving it. That's because your right eye sees more to the right of your finger, while your left eye sees more to the left. When both of your eyes are open, your brain combines these images, but when one eye is closed, the images don't combine into one, so it looks like your finger jumped.

# FROZEN FINGERS

　　Ask your grandchild to place his or her hands together, fingertip to fingertip. Bend both middle fingers down so they are touching the palms. Now place a coin between the tips of the child's ring fingers and ask him/her to drop the coin. It's not possible! That's because the muscles that control the ring fingers also control the middle fingers, and with the middle fingers held down, those muscles can't move.

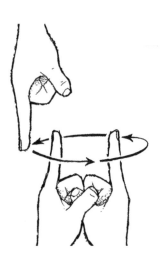

# MOVING FINGERS

　　Put your fists together with the fingers touching each other. Then lift both index fingers straight up so you are pointing at the sky. Have your grandchild stand in front of you and twirl their index finger very fast around your index fingers. Your fingers will automatically move closer together!

**Have you ever wondered what chairs would look like if your knees bent the other way?**

Ask the kids to imagine and design a chair!

# X-RAY VISION

Hold a paper-towel tube or rolled-up piece of paper in your right hand. Hold it up to your right eye and look through the tube, keeping both eyes open. Place your left hand fingers pointing up and palm facing you, against the side of the tube. Look at your hand and you can see right through it! Your x-ray vision is caused by each eye recording a separate image and putting them together—in this case, the palm of one hand and the hole in the tube.

## SUPER STRENGTH

Sit in a chair and have someone put their finger against your forehead. Try to stand up without using your hands. You can't! Your friend's finger is keeping you in your chair. This happens because you need to lean forward to get out of a chair without using your hands, and even the lightest pressure from your friend's finger stops you from doing so.

# I'M FALLING!

Have your grandchild lie face down on the floor and relax. Now you or his sibling lift up his legs at about a 45-degree angle and hold them there for two minutes. Then lower his legs to the floor. It will feel to the kiddo like he's falling right through the floor!

# FACE FACTS!

These amazing facts about the human face will give the kids a kick. Try out each of these theories by testing them out on each other, or by looking in the mirror (you can use a ruler, but measuring with the thumb and index finger work just fine). It's wild how often these face facts are true, no matter our age differences! (except for babies...they have to grow into their heads yet).

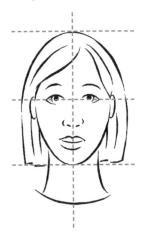

**WHERE'S THE MIDDLE OF THE FACE?**

Measure from the very top of the head to the bottom of the chin. Right in the middle of that space is where your eyes are! Yes, almost always, the bridge of the nose, between the eyes, will be the middle marker.

**HOW WIDE IS THE SPACE BETWEEN YOUR EYES?**

Measure the distance from the outer corner to the inner corner of your eye. Now place that same measurement between your two eyes. Almost always, the space between the eyes is the distance of one eye!

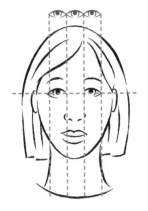

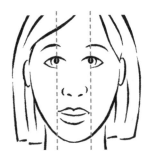

**HOW WIDE IS THE MOUTH?**

Here's a great amazing fact that is almost always true. Look at each side of the mouth. Now measure a straight line up from each side and it will line up with the pupil of the eye above.

## WHAT'S THE DISTANCE FROM THE BRIDGE TO THE BOTTOM OF THE NOSE?

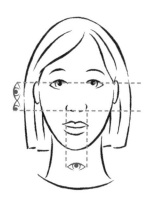

One and one half eye width! Now check the distance of the "parentheses" that are on either side of the nostrils. Yes, the distance from one side of the nostril to the other is one eye width.

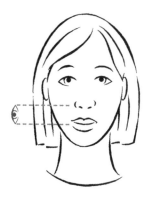

## WHAT IS THE DISTANCE BETWEEN THE BOTTOM OF THE NOSE AND THE BOTTOM PART OF THE UPPER LIP?

One eye width. Typically, the lower lip is thicker than the upper lip. The lips are thickest at the middle and taper to the corners.

## HERE'S ONE MORE:
## HOW SKINNY IS YOUR NECK?

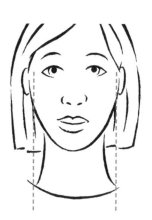

So often we think of a skinny little neck holding our heads up. It is actually thicker and stronger than you would normally think. Find the point where the bottom of the ear connects to the jaw. Now run your fingers down to where the neck connects to the shoulder. You will probably find that point is almost the same width as the space from ear to ear.

It's fun to test out all these amazing face facts on different people. For kids (and grandparents!) who like to draw, these guidelines can make a big difference in your next drawing.

**WOW! A person can make over 10,000 different facial expressions!!!**

How many can you make?

## THE HEAD TRICK

Stand against a wall and check out this theory: An average human's height is seven times the height of his or her head (except for very young children). See how many times this fact is true for the grandkids.

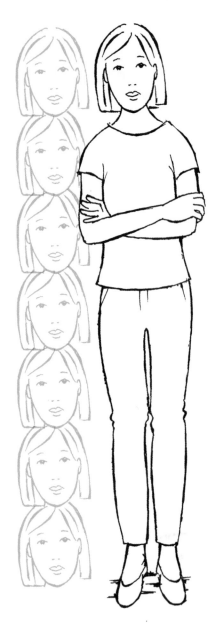

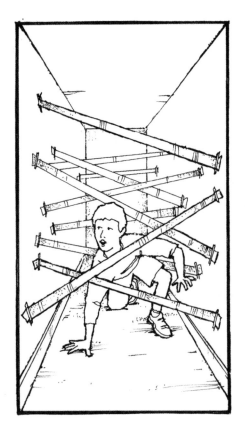

## LASER MAZE

It's a rainy day, the grandkids are bored, what's a grandma to do? Whip out the roll of red crepe paper, or strings, and some tape and make a crazy laser maze! Down a hallway, zig zag the crepe paper back and forth, high and low, taping onto the wall. Now challenge the grandkids to make their way through the laser beams without ever touching them! Step over, crawl under, find out how flexible your body can be to escape the maze!

# USE YOUR 5 SENSES!

Start at the beginning and find your way through this maze, being aware of each of the 5 senses that you will take along the journey as you go.

**FUN FACT:** Your ears and your nose never stop growing!

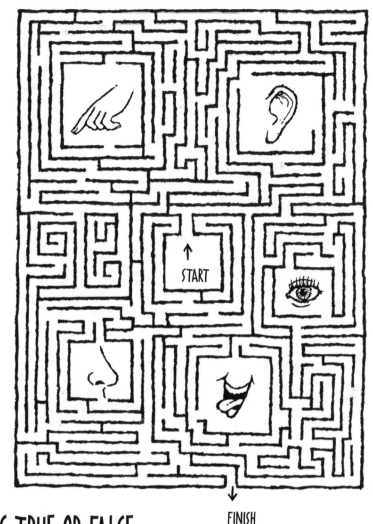

# THE AMAZING SENSES TRUE OR FALSE

Circle the correct answer.

1. **T F** The human eye can see a candle light 1.6 miles away.

2. **T F** Humans can smell feelings.

3. **T F** The tongue has its own unique "fingerprint".

4. **T F** Humans don't have tiny hairs in their ears that help them hear.

5. **T F** The skin is the biggest organ of the body.

Solutions in the back.

# CHAPTER 2: FUN WITH FOOD

*Cooking together is a grandma tradition as old as time. But we bet most grandmas won't dare to try the fun food experiments we've included in this chapter! So put down the cookbook, prepare to get messy, and see what happens when cooking and science meet!*

## SODA TRICK

Soda and milk do NOT go together! Take a 20-oz. bottle of cola and pour out about 1/4 of the bottle. Fill the bottle with milk. Replace the cap and shake the bottle as hard as you can. The milk will curdle and separate from the cola.

**VOLCANIC ERUPTION!**

For a really dramatic trick, make a diet soda and salt volcano! This trick makes a big fun mess, so do it ouside.

**You Will Need:**
- Cup of salt
- One two-liter bottle of diet soda

**Step 1:** Open a two-liter bottle of diet soda.

**Step 2:** Pour some salt slowly into the bottle a little at a time.

**Step 3:** Jump back, because the volcano will erupt in a crazy fountain of soda!

**Q: What's full of holes but still holds water?**

A: A sponge.

**The only fruit that has seeds on the outside is:**
**A. Pineapple   B. Kiwi   C. Strawberry**

# METAL MAGIC

This little experiment will seem like magic to the kids. You need something metal such as tarnished silver earrings. Fill a small bowl with lemon-lime soda. Hang the earrings on the edge of the bowl so they are submerged in the soda. Watch as the soda cleans the tarnish off the earrings and makes them sparkle like new! An amazing transformation right before your eyes. Your grandkids may have jewelry or items they would like to clean up, too.

# KETCHUP TO THE RESCUE

This is another way to mesmerize the kids with a metallic transformation. Tomatoes, which are the main ingredient in ketchup, contain acid just like soda does. Find a tarnished silver object, such as a bowl or pitcher. Using a paper towel let the kids rub ketchup all over the silver! Let it sit for half an hour. When they wipe off the ketchup to discover the shiny silver underneath, you'll hear lots of "oohs", "ahhs" and "Cool, Grandma!"

# MAKING BUTTERMILK

You're right in the middle of making biscuits for the kids and find that you don't have the buttermilk it calls for. Show the kids your resourcefulness! All you need to do is mix one tablespoon of lemon juice OR one tablespoon of white vinegar into a cup of milk. In five or ten minutes the kids can see the change. The acid in the lemon juice or vinegar will curdle the milk and make buttermilk.

# FREEZE!

Here's a quick, tricky way to instantly freeze a bottle of water. Fill a bowl halfway with ice cubes. Then cover the ice with some rock salt. Place a water bottle on top and cover it with more ice and rock salt. Let the bottle sit for five minutes. Remove the bottle and slam it on a hard surface such as a concrete sidewalk. Bam! You now have a bottle full of crushed ice.

# FANCY FEAST

Do you like chocolate-covered strawberries? It's easy to make them at home. Simply melt chocolate and pour it into an ice cube tray. Then place a strawberry in each compartment so half of it sits in the chocolate. Chill the tray in the fridge just till hardened, about 15-30 minutes. Then remove from the tray and enjoy immediately, or store in an airtight container in another cool place. (The fridge is too cold and can make the chocolate taste chalky.)

**I dropped a jar of pickles on the floor – but that's okay. I can dill with it.**

# VOILA! FROM GREEN TO RIPE... OVERNIGHT.

Do you have some tomatoes that aren't ripe yet? Send a very ripe banana to the rescue! Place the tomatoes and the banana in a plastic container. Close the lid and let it sit overnight. When you check on the tomatoes the next day, they will be ripe! That's because the ripe banana gives off a gas called ethylene that makes fruit ripen.

# FOLLOWING THE BOUNCING BERRY

Fresh ripe cranberries bounce. And apples float. (That's because they are 25 percent air.) Just some little fun facts for you to try out.

# SUPER-FLUFFY EGGS

Show the kids how to make the fluffiest eggs in the world! All you need is some sparkling water. Have them whisk eggs and sparkling water in a small bowl, then watch you as you pour the eggs into a hot pan and cook like an omelet. The carbonation in the water will puff up the eggs to super size. Yum!

# EGGS ON EDGE

There is a myth that you can make an egg stand on its end on the first day of spring. Actually, you can do it any day of the year. Simply pour a pile of salt on the table and balance the egg on top. Carefully remove the salt a little at a time by blowing through a straw. If you are patient and don't rush, eventually almost all of the salt will be gone and just a few grains will hold up the egg.

# EGG-ZACTLY!

Engage the kids in these egg tests.

Have you ever hard-boiled some eggs and then mixed them up with uncooked eggs? There's an easy way to tell if an egg is hard-boiled or not. Just lay the egg flat on the counter, then spin it. A hard-boiled egg will spin easily, but an uncooked egg will wobble.

How about a way to figure out if an egg is fresh or spoiled? Place the egg in a bowl of water. A fresh egg will sink. A spoiled egg will float.

# REAL OR FAKE?

When you're sharing biscuits or something else with honey, do this little trick on the side, and you'll be able to test if your honey is real or fake. It's true, not all honey is the real thing. Some honey is actually sugar water. Simply squeeze some honey in a bowl. Pour a little warm water into the bowl and swirl it around. If the honey is real, it will create a honeycomb pattern in the water. If it's fake, the "honey" will just ripple. Busted!

# "DON'T CRY OVER A CRACKED PLATE"

A cracked plate might bring tears and worry a grandkid. This trick can turn those tears into cheers of amazement. The plate has to be made of porcelain. Tape the cracks. Put the plate in a container and pour enough warm milk over the plate to cover it completely. Let the plate sit in the milk for two days. Then pour off the milk. Your plate looks as good as new! How does this work? Milk contains a protein called casein. When casein hardens, it becomes like plastic and fills in the cracks.

**Q: If there are three apples and you take away two, how many do you have?**

A: If you take two apples, than of course you have two.

# MAKE YOUR OWN ICE CREAM

Imagine! The kids can make their own ice cream—right in a plastic bag!

You will need:
- 1 cup half-and-half
- 2 tablespoons sugar
- 1/2-teaspoon vanilla extract
- 3 cups of ice
- 1/3-cup kosher salt
- Small plastic sandwich bag
- Large plastic storage bag

Step 1: Combine half-and-half, sugar, and vanilla in the small plastic bag. Push out excess air and seal.

Step 2: Combine ice and salt in the large plastic bag.

Step 3: Place the small bag inside the bigger bag and shake really, really hard for at least ten minutes, until the ice cream has hardened. Let the kiddos take turns.

Step 4: Add your favorite toppings and enjoy!

# A HEALTHY FROZEN SNACK

If you have a grandchild who is lactose intolerant, you can really give them a surprise with this idea. For a delicious, dairy-free, gluten-free treat, try this recipe using a surprise ingredient—bananas!

All you have to do is peel a few bananas and place them in the freezer until they are frozen solid. Then place the bananas in a blender and mix well. You can eat the banana right away if you like it soft-serve consistency. Or store it in an airtight container if you like your frozen treat harder. Either way, it's delicious—and healthy!

# MILK AND POPCORN SURPRISE

Maybe you have a little popcorn left over after watching the kids' favorite movie. So ask the kids, "do you think you can add popcorn to a full glass of milk without spilling anything? Let's find out!"

**Step 1:** Fill a glass to the top with milk.

**Step 2:** Fill an identical glass to the top with popped popcorn.

**Step 3:** Transfer the popcorn to the glass of milk a few pieces at a time. You can press the popcorn down in the glass if you want.

Does any of the milk spill out?

# FOODIE CREATIONS

Your kids will have great creative fun exploring how different fruits and vegetables look like characters, animals, flowers, and all kinds of things—with a little artistic help. If they grocery shop with you, let the kids look through the produce for items that inspire them. What face do you see in a green pepper? What shape does a yam remind you of? And what are those dance moves the little chilies seem to be doing?

Then help them create their vision! You will need to do the cutting for them using a small knife, following their directions. Common items that might be helpful additions are toothpicks, cloves, raisins, carrot and celery pieces, etc.

### Gourd Critter
Use a squash or gourd and with the simplest of additions—raisins and a cut-out mouth—you can make a sweet, silly or scary face.

### Little Pup
Use carrots and add pieces of the greens for ears and tail. Use toothpicks to hold together, and for legs.

### Mouse
With a lemon, cut out half oval shapes and lift to make some little ears. Don't cut all the way through. Use cloves for eyes, add a lemon peel sliver or carrot curl for the tail.

# MILKY COLOR EXPLOSION

It's art time, kids! Create a work of art using milk and dish soap!

You will need:
• Baking dish with a flat bottom
• Whole milk
• Dish soap
• Food coloring

Step 1: Fill the dish with about 1/2-inch of milk.

Step 2: Squirt food coloring into the milk to make big dots of color.

Step 3: Add one drop of dish soap in the middle of the milk.
        Watch what happens!

The sinking, swirling colors occur because milk is made of fat droplets in liquid. The dish soap separates the fat from the liquid. That makes the colored droplets rush together to create colorful blobs.

# GOOD FOOD, GOOD EATS

Grandma, ask your grandkids to fill in the blanks. Maybe they'll surprise you with their answers!

My favorite food is _____!

Here's how you make it: _____

_____. I like to eat it when

_____,

and I especially like the way _____ fixes it.

# FOLLOW THE FOOD CHAIN!

Follow the line through the loop-de-loops and twisty turns going over and under to match up each food with its logical partner.

**FUN FACT:**
Americans eat 50 billion hamburgers every year! That's a stack high enough to go to the moon!!

Spaghetti

Ice cream

Peanut butter

Chocolate sauce

Jelly

Meatballs

# WACKY FOODS TRUE OR FALSE

Circle the correct answer.

1. **T F** Spaghetti grows on trees.

2. **T F** Honey never goes bad.

3. **T F** The biggest pizza ever made used 4000 pounds of cheese.

4. **T F** There are over 350 shapes of pasta.

5. **T F** Chicken earlobes can predict what color egg they will lay.

Solutions in the back.

# CHAPTER 3: CRAZY SCIENCE FUN

*Science isn't just for school anymore. And we bet you never did most of these crazy experiments back in your school days! Have fun playing and learning with your grandkids with this collection of crazy fun.*

## MAKE OOBLECK!

Oobleck is a weird substance that has the properties of both liquids and solids. You can put your hand in oobleck just like you can dip your hand in water. But you can also squeeze the oobleck into a ball. Here's an easy recipe for you and the kids to make this weird slimy stuff.

You Will Need:
• 2 cups of cornstarch
• 1 cup of water
• Bowl
• Food coloring (optional)

Step 1:  Combine the cornstarch and water in the bowl.

Step 2:  Have the kids mix the ingredients together with their hands until you have oobleck!

If your oobleck is too watery, add a little more cornstarch. If it is too stiff, add a little more water. You can also add food coloring if you want to make oobleck in different colors.

# MAGIC WATERCOLOR BUTTERFLIES

Everyone knows you can combine colors to make new colors (think red plus blue equals purple, for example). But did you know you can separate colors too? This process is called chromatography. Here's a fun chromatography craft to share with your grandkids.

You will need:
- Newspaper
- Non-permanent markers
- White coffee filters
- Pencil
- Cups of water
- Black pipe cleaners
- String
- Scissors

**Step 1:** Cover the table with newspaper.

**Step 2:** Place one coffee filter on the newspaper. Use a marker to draw a thick circle around the center of the coffee filter where the ridged part meets the flat center.

**Step 3:** Fold the coffee filter in half and then in half again. You should have a cone shape.

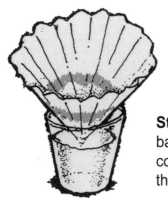

**Step 4:** Pull apart the cone-shaped filter and balance it on a glass of water. The tip of the cone should just touch the water. Be sure that the marker circle does NOT go into the water.

**Step 5:** Watch what happens as the filter absorbs the water and the water travels up to the colored circle.

**Step 6:** After the water has reached the outer edge of the coffee filter, place it on a newspaper to dry.

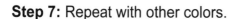

**Step 7:** Repeat with other colors.

To make your colored circles into a butterfly, scrunch up the middle of a coffee filter and wrap a black pipe cleaner around the center. Trim and bend the pipe cleaners to make antennae.

**Fluttering butterfly flies with a flutter for a flower.**
Say that three times super fast!

# RAINBOW IN A GLASS

Rainbows outside are pretty special. You and the kids can create your own rainbow right in the kitchen!

What You Need:
- Sugar
- Water
- Food coloring (red, yellow, green, and blue)
- Tablespoon
- 4 small clear plastic cups
- 1 large clear plastic cup

Step 1:  Line up the 4 small cups in a row. Add one tablespoon of sugar to the first cup. Add two tablespoons of sugar to the second cup. Add three to the third cup and four to the fourth cup. Leave the fifth (larger) cup empty for now.

Step 2:  Add 3 tablespoons of water to each of the first four cups. Stir until the sugar dissolves. If the sugar doesn't dissolve completely, add a little more water.

Step 3:  Add 2-3 drops of red food coloring to the first cup. Add 2-3 drops of yellow food coloring to the second cup. Add green food coloring to the third cup, and blue food coloring to the fourth. Stir each solution.

Step 4: Fill the large empty cup about one-fourth full of the blue sugar solution.

Step 5: Carefully layer some green sugar solution above the blue liquid. To do this, put a spoon in the glass just above the blue layer. Then pour the green solution slowly over the back of the spoon. If you do this right, you won't disturb the blue solution much at all. Add green solution until the glass is about half full.

Step 6: Layer the yellow solution above the green liquid, using the back of the spoon. Fill the cup to three-quarters full.

Step 7: Layer the red solution above the yellow liquid. Fill the glass the rest of the way. You have a rainbow in a glass!

Your rainbow exists because of density. Adding sugar makes the water in the cups more dense. Since some cups have more sugar, that solution is more dense than the solution in cups with less sugar.

**Q: What is at the end of the rainbow?**
A: W

# WALKING WATER

Here's a simple experiment showing the effects of absorption and blending colors.

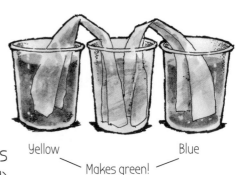

Yellow           Blue

Makes green!

You will need:

- 3 small clear glass jars or glasses (jelly type canning jars work well)
- Paper towels
- Water
- Food coloring

Set the three glasses sided by side on the counter or table. Fill the two outside glasses 2/3 way with water, then add 3 or so drops of different food coloring to each. Leave the middle glass empty. If using primary colors, you will have a good way of demonstrating how they blend to create secondary colors. (For example, use blue and yellow to create green in the middle glass; red and blue make purple; yellow and red make orange).

Fold a paper towel several times longways so it creates a kind of long "cord". Stick one end of the paper towel in the first glass and the other end in the middle glass. Repeat this with another paper towel, and place one end in the third glass, the other end in the middle glass. Now watch. In just a couple minutes you should see the colored water "walk" its way up the paper towel and begin to fill the middle glass. This could take 30 minutes or so. When done, the middle glass will show a new color blended from the two outer glass colors.

# CLOUD IN A JAR

Spend some relaxing daydream time with grandkids, just laying back and watching the clouds. Point out the shapes you each can see. Then while thinking about the awesomeness of clouds, go inside and make a cloud in a jar!

You will need:
• Jar with a lid
• 1/3 cup hot water
• Ice cubes
• Hairspray

**Step 1:** Pour the hot water into the jar. Swirl the water around so it warms up the sides.

**Step 2:** Turn the lid upside-down and place it on top of the jar.

**Step 3:** Place as many ice cubes as you can fit into the jar lid. Let them sit for about 20 seconds.

**Step 4:** Remove the lid and quickly spray some hairspray into the jar.

**Step 5:** Place the upside-down lid and ice back on top of the jar. You'll see a cloud form inside!

Clouds form when warm air and cold air meet. That's exactly what you did when you placed the ice on top of the warm water in the jar. Water vapor escaping from the hot water condensed when it hit the cold jar lid. The hairspray gave the water vapor something to hold on to. That allowed the vapor to condense, which created the cloud.

If you want to watch your cloud escape, just open the jar and let it disappear into the air.

# TORNADO IN A BOTTLE

Here's a quick and easy way to create a mini-tornado. Simply find a clean soda bottle and remove the label. Fill the bottle about three-quarters full with water. Add a drop of dishwashing liquid. If you want, add a few drops of food coloring or some glitter to make your tornado easier to see. Tightly cap the bottle, turn it upside-down, and hold it by the neck. Then swing the bottle around in a circular motion. Stop and look. Can you see a tornado swirling around inside?

Your mini-tornado forms because of centripetal force. That force directs the water toward the center of its circular path and creates a funnel.

# SPINNING CAN

This just doesn't seem to make sense, but it really works. If you have a group of kids together, they will love taking turns trying this out.

**Step 1:** Pour up to 1/2-cup of water into an empty soda can, enough to fill it 1/5 full. (You might have to try different amounts to find the right balance.)

**Step 2:** Balance the can on the edges of the bottom rim. Let go, and the can will stand up!

**Step 3:** Gently push the side of the can near the top. The can will spin around and not fall!

# FLOATING CARDBOARD

Take this fun and silly experiment outside on a hot day. Nope, you're not supposed to get wet, but...you know how things go!

Step 1: Fill a rigid plastic cup all the way to the top with water.

Step 2: Place a square of thin cardboard on top of the cup. (The cardboard should be wider than the width of the cup's top.) Slide it around so it gets a little wet.

Step 3: Put one hand on top of the cardboard and the other hand on the bottom of the cup.

Step 4: Quickly flip the cup upside-down!

Step 5: Take your hand away from the cardboard. It will stay in place and hold the water inside the cup too. Why? There is more air pressure outside the cup than inside (because the water takes up all the space), so the air pressure keeps the cardboard in place.

# BALANCING ACT

Get a little silly and spend more time around the table after your next meal. The grandkids will think you are pretty cool when they see you accomplish this.

Step 1: Place a heavy glass on the table.

Step 2: Find a fork and spoon that are the same weight. Wedge them together so the outside tines of the fork are on one side of the spoon and the middle tines are on the other. You should end up with an arch shape.

Step 3: Slide the end of a unlit match between the tines of the fork so most of the match is sticking out under the arch.

Step 4: Carefully balance the match on the edge of the glass. The fork and spoon handles should curve around the glass. You might need to try this a few times to get it to work!
This trick works because the middle of the match is the center of gravity for the whole contraption.

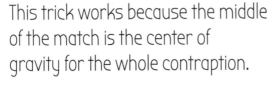

# STATIC SPIN

Ok, Super Grandma, you want a REAL challenge, one that will keep the kids occupied for a good long time? Good luck with this one!

You will need:
- Two coins
- Plastic cup
- Wooden match
- Plastic spoon

**Step 1:** Place a coin flat on the table. Stand the second coin on top of the first.

**Step 2:** Balance the match on top of the standing coin.

**Step 3:** Put a plastic cup over the coins and match.

**Step 4:** Rub the plastic spoon over your hair. (This works best on clean, dry hair.)

**Step 5:** Move the spoon steadily around the cup. The matchstick will move with the spoon. This trick works because rubbing the spoon against your hair created static electricity. Static causes the tiny atoms in the spoon to act like a magnet and attract atoms in other objects. The force is strong enough to move the match.

# MATCHSTICK MATH

Challenge those whiz kids with this one! Move just ONE of the matchsticks in this equation to make it true.

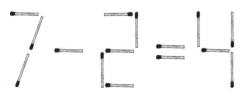

Solutions in the back.

# FROZEN BUBBLES

Have your supplies on hand so when the grandkids are around when the temperature gets below 32° you're ready to wow them with this magical project.

You will need:

- Jars
- 2 cups distilled hot water
- 1/2 cup dish soap
- 1/2 cup corn syrup
- Food coloring
- Picture frame with glass (you can pick one up at a second hand store)
- Bubble wands (usually found at craft or party supply stores)
- Bowl
- Camera

**Step 1:** Make the bubble mixture by combining hot water, dish soap, and corn syrup in a bowl. Then pour mixture in to jars. Add food coloring, if desired, to make different-colored mixtures. Stir slowly to mix. Let the mixtures sit in jars overnight.

**Step 2:** Lay the picture frame flat on a table outside in a sheltered, cold area.

**Step 3:** Coat the glass of the frame with bubble soap so the bubbles will stick and not pop.

**Step 4:** Blow bubbles and place them on the glass. Then watch and wait. If the air is cold enough (the colder the better!), it will freeze the soap and your bubbles! But they won't last for long so grab your camera and capture the magic!

# UNDER PRESSURE

After you have that hot cocoa with the kids, use those extra mini marshmallows to do something spontaneous, silly and surprising. Watch a funny marshmallow head change shape and expression due to the results of air pressure.

You will need:
- Mini marshmallows  • Fine line marker
- Dosing syringe big enough to fit a mini marshmallow inside (This is the type of dispenser you use if you've given liquid medicine to a child or pet. It has no needle. Available at the pharmacy.)

Step 1: Draw a face on the marshmallow. It's not only cute, but it will also help you see how the marshmallow changes under pressure.

Step 2: Remove the plunger from the syringe and place a marshmallow inside. Replace the plunger and seal the tip with your finger.

Step 3: Pull on the plunger to decrease the air pressure. What happens to the marshmallow?

Step 4: Push the plunger back in. Now what happens? The air pressure increased inside the syringe. This makes the marshmallow—which is full of air pockets—get smaller. Decreasing the air pressure (as in step 3) makes the marshmallow get bigger.

# ICE CANDLE

Grandma, be sure to be cautious with the candle while children are close by.

You will need:
• Metal or glass bowl
• Water
• Paper cup
• Rock
• Cutting board
• Tealight candle

**Step 1:** Fill the bowl with one or two inches of water. Put it in the freezer.

**Step 2:** After the water has frozen, set the paper cup on the ice. Place the rock inside the cup as a weight to hold the cup in place.

**Step 3:** Fill the bowl with more water (keep the water level below the lip of the cup), and freeze.

**Step 4:** Remove the bowl of ice from the freezer and tear out the paper cup. It will leave a hole.

**Step 5:** Flip the bowl onto the cutting board. Rub your hands over the outside of the bowl to warm the ice so it falls out of the bowl. Turn the "ice bowl" right-side up.

**Step 6:** Insert the candle into the hole. Gather the kiddos while Grandma lights the candle.

**Step 7:** If you want, make several ice candles and float them in a big bowl of water for a pretty effect!

The ice acts like glass to magnify and reflect the light. This creates a lamp that is brighter than the candle would be on its own.

**Q: I'm tall when I'm young and I'm short when I'm old. What am I?**

A: A candle.

# BOTTLE BLOBS

You probably know that oil and water don't mix. This project uses that scientific principle to create a cool and colorful show.

You Will Need:
- Clean 2-liter soda bottle
- 3/4 cup of water
- Measuring cup
- Vegetable oil
- Food coloring
- Fizzing tablets with sodium bicarbonate (Many common brands of this gas and tummy reliever can be found in the grocery store or drug store.)

**Step 1:** Pour the water into the bottle.

**Step 2:** Use the measuring cup to slowly pour the vegetable oil into the bottle until the bottle is almost full. Wait until the oil and water separate, with the oil rising to the top.

**Step 3:** Add 10 drops of food coloring. It will sink through the oil into the water below.

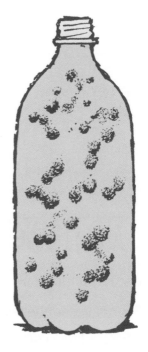

**Step 4:** Break a tablet in half and drop it into the bottle. Then watch as the oil forms into colorful blobs. This happens because the fizzing tablet releases gas, which moves the colored water around. Since oil and water don't mix, the oil forms into drops instead of being dissolved in the water. If you want to continue the blobby fun, just add another half of a tablet. You can even seal up the bottle of water and oil to play with later.

# SAVE THE OCEANS!

Millions of sea animals die every year due to "marine debris" ... plastic, trash, hooks, nets and lines. You are the futuristic marine agent who has to blast your way through this maze to recharge your neutron blaster to continue the cleanup.

**FUN FACT:**
Earth's biggest waterfall is in the ocean. It's called the Denmark straight and has a drop of 11,500 feet.

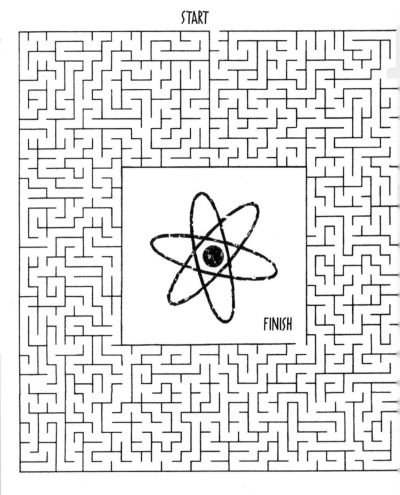

START

FINISH

# ODD AND STRANGE TRUE OR FALSE

Circle the correct answer.

1. **T F** Hot water freezes faster than cold water.

2. **T F** Your brain can process over 70,000 thoughts in a day.

3. **T F** 41 new species are discovered each day by scientists.

4. **T F** The moon is made of cheese.

5. **T F** There were only 23 hours in a day during the dinosaur age.

Solutions in the back.

# CHAPTER 4: WEIRD WEATHER

Mother Nature has done some crazy things over the years. Here are some of the weirdest weather events:

# IT'S RAINING...FROGS?

Tornadoes and other storms have been known to gather up animals and set them down in other places. This phenomenon has led to the sky unleashing frogs, fish, and other small water creatures. Scary, to be sure, but harmless (except for those poor frogs!).

# THE SUPERSTORM

In March 1993, one of the most destructive storms to ever hit the United States spread bad weather all over the eastern part of the nation. "The Storm of the Century" created storm surges and flooding in Florida, heavy snow from Alabama to Maine, and the closure of all airports on the East Coast for the first time ever.

**Q: What do you call a friend who falls into a puddle?**

A: A muddy buddy!

# BLOOD RAIN

In 2015, residents in Spain were terrified when blood began raining from the sky. It turned out the rain had mixed with an algae that colored the liquid red.

# ROLL OUT THE CLOUDS

Clouds come in different sizes and shapes, but few are as weird-looking as a roll cloud. A roll cloud is a low, tube-shaped cloud that appears to roll slowly across the sky. One type, called the Morning Glory, can be up to 600 miles long, a mile high, and move as fast as 38 miles per hour just 300-600 feet above the ground. They only form regularly on the Gulf of Carpentaria in Australia. These clouds don't unleash any storms, but they sure do look strange! Help your grandchild visualize what a mile high cloud 600 miles long would look like!

# BUGNADO?

You've heard of tornadoes, but what about a bugnado? These creepy incidents happen when hot air pushes upward into colder air and creates a spinning vortex that sucks bugs out of the air and sends them swirling around and around.

# HAIL IN HAWAII?

Hail is made of ice, but it can fall during thunderstorms at any time of year, even in the middle of summer. And it can fall in any place. This was proved on March 9, 2012, when a big chunk of hail, about the size of a softball fell in Oahu, Hawaii. The storm dropped other hailstones measuring 2- to 3-inches in diameter as well.

# A SOGGY ISLAND

Few places on Earth receive as much rain as Réunion Island, about 500 miles east of Madagascar. In January 1980, Tropical Cyclone Hyacinthe stalled near the island for about two weeks. The storm dumped an incredible 239.49 inches, or almost 20 feet, of rain in 15 days. Show the kids what twenty feet looks like.

# SUPER SNOW

New England is used to big snowstorms, but the winter of 2014-2015 proved to be too much even for that snowy part of the country. Between January 24 and February 22, 2015, Boston received just under 8 feet of snow. Maybe that's about the height of your ceiling, to help the kids visualize.

# TOO MANY TORNADOES

The largest tornado outbreak in history occurred between April 25-28, 2011. A record 362 tornadoes struck the South and Midwest. They caused destruction in 13 states, including Alabama, Arkansas, Louisiana, Georgia, Tennessee, Virginia, Mississippi, Kentucky, Illinois, Missouri, Ohio, Texas, and Oklahoma. One scientist tracked a photograph picked up from by tornado winds in Alabama to where it landed in Tennessee, 220 miles away. June 3, 1980, also know as "The Night of the Twisters: was in Grand Island, Nebraska. The town was hit by not one, not two, but seven tornadoes in less than three hours that one night.

# ONE WINDY DAY...

Here's a clever mind twister for your little future engineers! An electric train is traveling at 80 miles per hour northwest toward a tunnel. The blustery winds on this day are blowing southeast at 80 miles per hour. Which direction does the smoke blow?

Solutions in the back.

**Q: Why do birds fly south for the winter?**

A: It's too far to walk.

# THAT'S HOT!

It was once thought that the hottest place on the planet was in El Azizia, Libya with a record temperature of 136 degrees in 1922. However, thanks to new advancements in technology and satelites there is a new winner for the "hottest place on earth" and it's the Lut desert located in Iran with a whopping, high temperature of 159 degrees in 2010. Most outdoor thermometers arent even capable of recording temperatures that hot!

# FIRE TORNADOES

A rare and terrifying event is known as a fire tornadoes and is a very destructive event. As hot air rises from the ground, it forms vertical columns, or "chimneys," until it becomes less dense, cools and then dissipates at higher altitudes. As more hot air is pulled into the rising column of fire, it begins to swirl violently in a vortex typical of a normal tornado. They don't usually last very long, but can cause additional fires and leave destruction in their path.

# SO MUCH SNOW

A total of 15.75 feet (189 inches) fell in the old Mount Shasta Ski Bowl in northern California. This is a record for a single storm and the most snow received in February, 1959.

# AMAZING FACTS ABOUT WEATHER ON THE MOON

Next time you have the grandkids for an overnight stay, go outside and do some sky gazing! Here is some amazing information to share about the moon.

On earth, we experience all kinds of weather. Wind, rain, hail, storms, snow, hurricanes, clouds and sunshine. The moon has no weather at all! It has no atmosphere. It has very weak gravity. It cannot keep gases that make up air. If you don't have air or gas, you can't have wind. Still, it does have ice! Hard to imagine how that happens, but it is thought that ice came from comet strikes.

The moon has day and night, hot and cold. Daytime on one side of the moon lasts almost 14 days, followed by the same number of dark nights. Temperatures can reach 260 degrees when sunlight hits the moon's surface. The temperature can drop to minus 280 degrees during the "dark side of the moon"! Brrrrrr.

**Q: In a one-story pink house, there was a pink person, a pink cat, a pink fish, a pink computer, a pink chair, a pink table, a pink telephone, a pink shower – everything was pink! What color were the stairs?**

A: There weren't any stairs, it was a one-story house.

# IT'S RAINING FROGS!

Wow, it's been a gully-washer and the frogs are everywhere. So hop to it, step carefully and find your way out of there!

**FUN FACT:**
Bolts of lightning can shoot out of an erupting volcano.

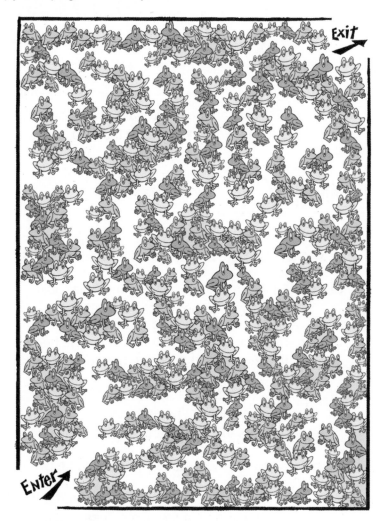

# STORMY AND WILD TRUE OR FALSE

Circle the correct answer.

1. **T F** Humans can't sneeze with their eyes open.

2. **T F** Certain frogs are the most poisonous animals in the world.

3. **T F** There are some snowflakes that are fifteen inches in diameter.

4. **T F** Only 1% of the water on earth can be consumed.

5. **T F** Cold weather causes bicycle tires to go flat.

Solutions in the back.

# CHAPTER 5: LET'S MAKE MAGIC

*"How did you do that, Grandma?!!" Kids will love trying to figure out how Grandma accomplished these tricks. Then you can teach them how to perform them to surprise others!*

## JUGGLING

Okay, so this isn't exactly a magic trick, but it will look like magic if you learn how to juggle! Here's a step-by-step routine to follow.

**Step 1:** Find some small balls or small beanbags. You don't want to start with anything heavy or breakable!

**Step 2:** Practice throwing the ball from one hand to the other. Work on tossing and catching the ball without looking.

**Step 3:** Now it's time to add a second ball. Hold a ball in each hand. Toss the ball in your right hand across to your left hand. While that ball is in the air, toss the ball in your left hand over to your right.

**Step 4:** Keep practicing until you can juggle two balls.

**Step 5:** Once juggling two balls is easy, add a third ball. Hold two balls in one hand and one in the other. Toss and catch them in order--right, left, right. One ball will always be in the air.

**Step 6:** Keep the balls low and in front of you. If you toss them up high, they will be harder to follow and catch.

**Step 7:** Keep practicing!

**Jules juggled jeweled jelly jugs.**

Say that three times super fast!

# MAGIC KNOT

For this trick, you will need a piece of rope about a yard long.

Step 1: Ask a grandchild to tie a knot without letting go of each end of the rope. It's impossible, right?

Step 2: When he or she gives up, take back the rope.

Step 3: Fold your arms so one hand is under your arm.

Step 4: Pick up one end of the rope in each hand.

Step 5: Keeping hold of the rope ends, unfold your arms to the side. Thus, you will pull the ends to make a magic knot!

# MAKE SOME CHANGE

Everyone would love to make money out of thin air! Here's how to do it.

Step 1: Show the kids your hands so they know your hands are empty.

Step 2: Rub your hands together. Open them to show a coin in the palm of one hand!

Where did the coin come from? Here's the trick.

Step 1: Before you show the kids your hands, place a coin in one palm and bend your fingers a little bit. The flesh of your palm will hold the coin in place. (Hint: Practice holding the coin this way before you start the trick!)

Step 2: When you show the audience your "empty" hands, be quick! Show one hand is empty by pointing at it with the other hand. As your fingers point, they will hide the coin in the other palm.

Step 3: Straighten your fingers as you rub your hands together. The coin will be revealed in your palm.

# THE DISAPPEARING CUP

Magicians don't just make things appear out of thin air. They can make things *disappear* too. Practice these steps several times to perfect this trick before you try it out on the kids!

**Action 1:** Sit at a table.

**Action 2:** Place a plastic cup upside down on the table.

**Action 3:** Cover the cup with a paper napkin that covers the entire cup well.

**Action 4:** Lift up the napkin and cup and slam it down on the table. Surprise!

The cup didn't break—it disappeared! All that's left is an empty napkin. ***Here's the secret!***

When you lay the napkin over the cup, form it tightly around the cup so it will hold the shape. As you are about to "lift" the cup and napkin, secretly move them to the edge of the table where you hold the napkin form in place while letting the cup quietly drop to your lap. Then pick up the napkin, keeping it in cup form even though it's empty! Quickly slap it down on the table before anyone realizes the cup is gone!

Practice your stealth until the cup drop is perfected!

**Q: What can run but can't walk?**

A: A drop of water.

# PREDICT THE CARD

A deck of cards is a great prop for a magician. Here is a trick that will have your grandkids thinking you can read their minds:

Step 1: Ask your grandkid to pick a card from a deck of cards. He or she should remember what the card is. Then he or she should slide the card back into the deck without showing you.

Step 2: Cut the deck several times to mix up the cards.

Step 3: Flip through the deck and pull out the card your grandchild picked.

How is this trick done? It's simple!

Step 1: Before you do the trick, go through the deck and place all the red cards together and all the black cards together in two halves.

Step 2: When the grandchild places the card back into the deck, make sure he or she puts it into the opposite half that it was taken from.

Step 3: No matter how many times you cut the deck, the chosen card will always be surrounded by cards of the opposite color. That makes it easy to find the card!

# LET'S MAKE MAGIC!

A real magician needs all the right accessories before the big performance. Find your way to the center, and collect all the things along the way that you will need.

**FUN FACT:**
The magic trick called the "cup and ball" has been around for over 5,000 years.

# MAGICALLY TRUE OR FALSE

Circle the correct answer.

1. **T F** The world's fastest magician once performed 255 effects in two minutes.

2. **T F** 10 decks of cards are printed every second.

3. **T F** You can get a college degree in magic.

4. **T F** A magician's moustache gives them good luck.

5. **T F** All magician's hats are sold with a rabbit.

Solutions in the back.

# CHAPTER 6: AMAZING ANIMALS

*Explore the world of the the animal kingdom with these wild facts. You can introduce the grandkids to amazing animal habits and adaptations by going to the zoo, playing games, or simply snuggling together to read these facts. (They'll really love the gross ones.)*

## ANIMAL WEAPONS

Some animals protect themselves by turning their bodies into weapons. Here are just a few of the crazy and pretty disgusting ways animals defend themselves.

• The horned lizard squirts blood out of its eyes.

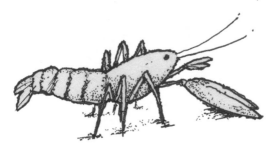

• The pistol shrimp can snap its claw so quickly it creates a pressure wave that creates a loud bang. That's a sure way to stun or scare away any predators!

• The Central American hairy frog can shove its foot bones through its toes to create super-sharp claws.

• Turning your bones into claws is crazy, but what about turning your ribs into dangerous spikes? The Spanish ribbed newt pushes its ribs through its chest to discourage predators. Here's another crazy fact—the newt's skin heals quicker than other animal bodies, so it doesn't take long to repair the cuts.

• Clown loaches are pretty, but watch out! These fish have sharp spines hidden under their eyes. These spines can shoot out to stab predators.

• Hagfish are a type of eel. When they are attacked, they release a slime that is so thick and gooey, it can coat the gills of predators so they choke to death.

• A species of termite in French Guinea will sacrifice itself to protect the colony. How? By turning into a bomb! Older members of the colony store up poisons throughout their lives. If the colony is threatened, the termites will blow themselves up to kill the attackers.

• Sea cucumbers spend much of their time just lying on the bottom of the sea. Easy prey, right? Wrong! When attacked, some sea cucumbers literally "spill their guts". Predators get a mouthful of sticky, toxic internal organs. Yuck! The sea cucumbers regenerate their organs quickly, in about one and a half to five weeks.

• There's no shame in running away from danger—especially if you can do it on water! The basilisk lizard can run on its back feet across the surface of water for up to 60 feet before sinking.

• To attract a mate, the hooded seal will close up one nostril and blow up the other one like a big red balloon. Because everyone wants a balloon-head for a partner, right?

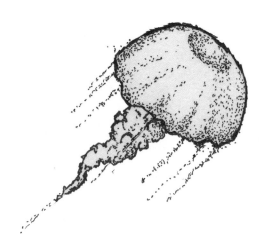

• Some jellyfish can turn back time! They can go back to an earlier stage of life called a polyp. In theory, that means a jellyfish could live forever. However, most are killed by disease or eaten by other animals before their time is up.

• A sea star's mouth is so small it can't swallow its prey. So it does the next best thing. The sea star grabs its prey, then pushes its stomach out of its mouth and digests its victim on the spot.

• The diving bell spider is the only spider that lives underwater. How does it breathe? Its web is like a bubble and can store oxygen. The spider can stay underwater for a whole day by breathing the air inside the bubble.

• The mimic octopus can make its body look like at least 15 different kinds of sea animals.

• Who needs lungs? Not the lungless frog of Borneo. This little creature breathes through its skin.

• It's no problem if a predator bites a gecko's tail. The tail—which is full of fat—simply breaks off. Sometimes the tail even twitches, which makes it look like a living animal. Meanwhile, the gecko runs away from its distracted attacker. Some geckos will regenerate their tails, some will not.

• The zombie worm is another sea creature with disgusting table manners. Instead of chewing and swallowing, the worm lays against its prey and secretes a toxic acid through its skin. The acid turns its victim into mush, which the zombie worm then absorbs through its skin.

**Q: A man was taking a walk outside when it started to rain. The man didn't have an umbrella, and he wasn't wearing a hat. His clothes got soaked, yet not a single hair on his head got wet. How could this happen?**

A: The man was bald.

# WHAT'S THE DIFFERENCE?

Sometimes it's hard to tell one animal from another. Next time you're at the zoo or a wildlife center, keep these facts in mind.

## ALLIGATORS VS. CROCODILES

Snout: Alligators have a wide, U-shaped snout. Crocodiles have a longer, pointed, V-shaped snout.

Teeth: An alligators teeth are usually hidden when its mouth is closed. A crocodile has a toothy grin.

Habitat: Alligators tend to live in freshwater habitats. Crocodiles prefer saltwater habitats.

## BUTTERFLIES VS. MOTHS

**Color:** Moths are usually drab in color. Butterflies are more brightly colored.

**Antennae:** A moth's antennae are usually feathery or look like combs. A butterfly's antennae are thin with club-shaped tips.

**Body:** Moths are wide and fuzzy. Butterflies are slender and smooth.

**Habits:** Moths are usually active at night. Butterflies are active during the day.

**Wings:** Moths usually rest with their wings open. Butterflies rest with their wings closed.

# HARES VS. RABBITS

**Size:** Hares are bigger than rabbits.
**Legs:** Hares have long legs. A rabbit's legs are shorter.
**Ears:** Hares have longer ears. Most rabbits have smaller ears.
**Color:** Hares change color with the seasons. Rabbits stay the same color all year long.
**Homes:** Hares make nests on the ground. Most rabbits dig burrows underground.
**Babies:** Baby hares are born with fur and with their eyes open. Baby rabbits are naked, blind and helpless.
**Food:** Hares like tough food, like bark and twigs. Rabbits prefer soft food, like grass and vegetables.
**Movement:** Hares make long leaps. Rabbits make short hops.
**Behavior:** Hares like to live alone. They cannot be kept as pets. Rabbits like to live in groups. They can be kept as pets.

# INSECTS VS. SPIDERS

Legs:   Insects have six legs. Spiders have eight.
Body:   An insect's body has three sections. A spider's has two.
Wings:  At some point in their lives, almost all insects have wings. Spiders never have wings.
Antennae: Insects have antennae. Spiders do not. The pair of appendages in front of their legs are pedipalps.

# FROGS VS. TOADS

**Skin:** A frog's skin is wet and slimy. A toad's skin is dry and rough.
**Body:** A frog's body is narrow. A toad's body is wide.
**Legs:** A frog has long back legs. A toad's legs are shorter.
**Eggs:** Frogs lay their eggs in fat clusters. Toads lay their eggs in long strings.
**Habitat:** Frogs usually live in water. Toads live outside of water.
**Eyes:** A frog's eyes are high on its head and tend to bulge out. A toad's eyes are lower on its head and are shaped more like footballs.
**Movement:** Frogs make long leaps. Toads make short hops.

# COYOTES VS. WOLVES

Head: A coyote's snout is narrow. Its nose is small but its ears are big and pointed. A wolf has a broad snout and a wider nose, but its ears are smaller and round.

Size: Wolves are heavier and longer than coyotes.

Sound: A coyote's howl is high and short. It also yips and barks. A wolf's howl is low and long.

# AFRICAN ELEPHANTS VS. ASIAN ELEPHANTS

Ears: Think of an elephant's ears as a map of their homeland. An African elephant's ears are large and stretch over the neck, just like the shape of Africa is long and wide. An Asian elephant's ears are smaller and look like the shape of India.

Weight: African elephants are a lot bigger than Asian elephants.

Heads: An African elephant's head is round and has a dome on top. An Asian elephant's head has two domes with a crease in the middle.

Lips: An African elephant has short, wide lips. An Asian elephant has long, thin lips.

Trunk: An African elephant's trunk has two "fingers" on the end. Its trunk is also softer and more heavily ringed than an Asian elephant's. An Asian elephant's trunk only has one "finger."

Tusks: All African elephants have tusks. Only about half of Asian elephants have small tusks.

# FIND THE CAT

See how quickly you can find the cat below...Go!
Did you know the fastest domestic housecat can run 30 mph?

# MONKEY TIME

How many monkeys are hiding in this pack of pug pups?

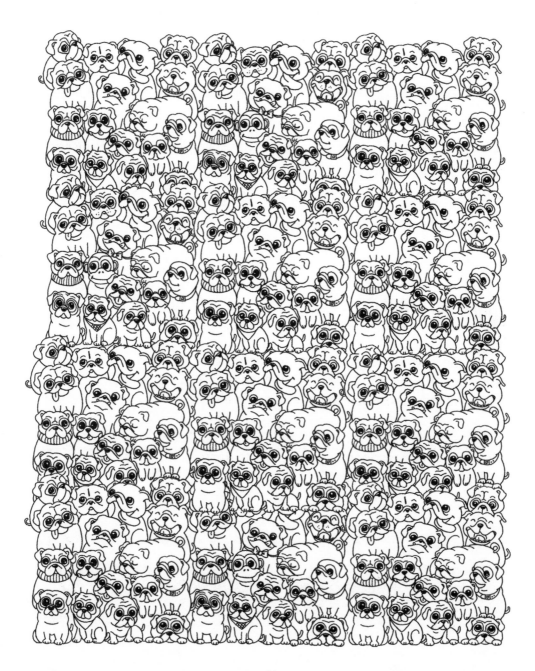

# CAN YOU HEAR ME NOW?

You probably know that animals and people hear by capturing sound waves in their ears. Bats and dolphins also do this, but they use their ears to "see"! This ability is called echolocation. Both bats and dolphins make high-pitched squeaking sounds. The sounds bounce off objects around the animal, then come back into their ears. This process helps the animals sense what is around them by the patterns the sound waves make when they bounce back. Echolocation helps bats find prey and obstacles in the dark. Dolphins use echolocation to find their way around underwater.

# BOUNCING SOUND

People have developed a way to use echolocation too. A system called sonar (short for **SO**und **NA**vigation and **R**anging) sends out sound waves underwater to see what is in the area.

Sonar is helpful for exploring and making nautical charts, locating underwater hazards for navigation, and to search for things on the seafloor such as shipwrecks!

**Q: Where is the ocean the deepest?**
A: At the bottom!

# PLAY THE ECHO GAME

This fun exercise will help grandkids understand the idea of navigating by hearing. So gather family and friends around.

Create an outside circle of those who will act as "Trees." They will be the boundary-keepers. If players start to cross the boundary, they will gently wave their "limbs" to guide them back inside.

Inside the circle, one grandchild is blindfolded and will be the Bat. Sure, tie on a cape (such as a half-apron) to help in playing the role. A few other kids are Moths and place themselves randomly in the circle. The Bat begins by making its own Batsound. It can be a high squeak. In response, the Moths echo with their own distinguishable sound. It could be a clicking sound. Each time the Bat squeaks, the Moths echo with clicks. The Bat uses only hearing to move locate and catch the Moths as they move around. The found Moth is "devoured" and moved silently to wait outside the circle. When all are found, the last-standing Moth takes over as Bat, and the other players change roles.

# BLUBBER GLOVES

Maybe the kids already know that a thick layer of fat called blubber helps whales, walruses, and other animals keep warm in freezing-cold water. Here's a way to experience blubber's warming effects for themselves.

You will need:
- Large plastic sealable storage bags (at least 1-quart size)
- Shortening (solid, not liquid)
- Nitrile gloves (the kind a doctor wears)
- Bucket of ice and water

Step 1:  Fill one bag 3/4 full of shortening.

Step 2:  Have a grandchild put on the gloves.

Step 3:  Insert one of the child's gloved hands in an empty bag and the other hand in the bag filled with shortening. Keep the sealable bags closed up to the wrist.

Step 4: Have the grandchild place his or her hands, submerging just to the top of their hands but not past the wrist, in the bucket of icy water for as long as they comfortably can.

Step 5: Which hand stays warmer?

# OH, HONEY!

Honey bees are amazing and hard-working creatures and extremely important to the ecosystem! It's understandable that finding bees in the yard can scare the kiddos. Here are 25 un-BEE-lievable facts about bees and honey that might give the kids a new appreciation for them.

1. Honey bees must gather nectar from two million flowers to make one pound of honey.

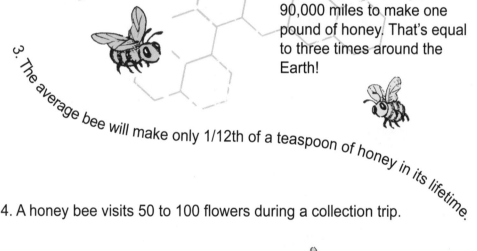

2. One bee has to fly about 90,000 miles to make one pound of honey. That's equal to three times around the Earth!

3. The average bee will make only 1/12th of a teaspoon of honey in its lifetime.

4. A honey bee visits 50 to 100 flowers during a collection trip.

5. A honey bee can fly for up to six miles, and as fast as 15 miles per hour.

6. A bee's brain is about the size of a sesame seed! That doesn't sound so smart, yet the bee can learn and remember things, and make calculations based on distance and food sources. It can even solve math problems!

65

7. A colony of bees consists of 20,000-60,000 honey bees and one queen.

8. All worker bees are female. Like their name says, worker bees are hard workers. They only live for about 6 weeks and pretty much work themselves to death.

9. The queen bee can live up to 5 years. She is the only bee that lays eggs. During the summer, a queen bee can lay up to 2,500 eggs per day.

10. Male honey bees are called drones. They are larger than worker bees, have no stingers, and do no work. Their only job is to mate with the queen.

11. Honey has always been highly regarded as a medicine. It is thought to help with everything from sore throats and digestive disorders to skin problems and hay fever.

12. Honey has antiseptic properties. History shows it was used as a dressing for wounds and a first aid treatment for burns.

13. Honey bees have been producing honey in the same way for 150 million years.

14. The honey bee is the only insect that produces food eaten by man.

15. Honey lasts an incredibly long time if stored properly. In fact, it will change into crystals that are still edible. In this state it's know as "candied".

16. The bees' buzz is the sound made by their wings which beat 11,400 times per minute.

17. When a bee finds a good source of nectar it flies back to the hive to tell its friends. To do this, the bee performs a dance which shows where the flower is in relation to the sun and the hive. This dance is called the "waggle dance."

18. Honey was part of Cleopatra's daily beauty ritual.

19. Honey is used in beauty products because it has a great ability to attract and retain moisture.

20. Honey is incredibly healthy. It includes enzymes, vitamins, minerals, and an antioxidant called pinocembrin which improves brain function.

21. Without bees, we would not have many fruits or vegetables. As bees visit flowers, they transfer pollen from one plant to another. This helps new plants to grow.

22. The U.S. government estimates that honey bees pollinate 80 percent of the nation's crops.

23. If the queen bee dies, workers create a new queen by selecting a newly hatched insect and feeding it a special food called "royal jelly." This jelly causes the larva to develop into a queen.

24. Only female bees (worker bees) have stingers. Honey bees are the only bees that die after stinging.

25. Honey bees have an amazing sense of smell. This helps them find the flowers they like to visit.

**Bonus Fact:** Wasps, yellow jackets, and hornets are NOT bees and they do not produce honey.

# TAKE AN OCEAN EXCURSION!

See if you can get to each site to see the cool marine life—but do stay away from those sharks!

**FUN FACT:** The largest wave ever surfed was 80 feet tall. That's as tall as 8 school busses stacked on top of each other.

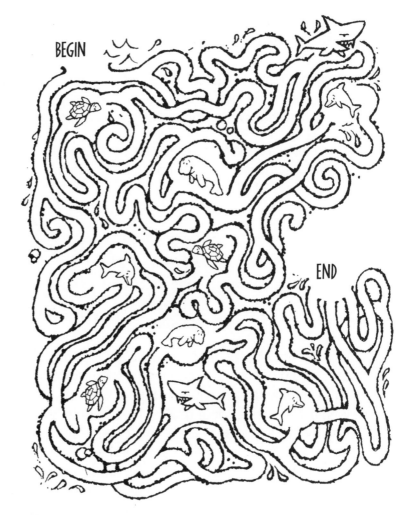

# DEEP BLUE TRUE OR FALSE

Circle the correct answer.

1. **T F** 94% of all life on earth lives in the ocean.

2. **T F** Jellyfish are more dangerous than sharks.

3. **T F** Seahorses sleep upside down.

4. **T F** More people have visited the moon than the ocean's deepest point.

5. **T F** There are waterfalls in the ocean.

Solutions in the back.

# UNDERWATER ANIMALS QUIZ

There's so much to learn about our friends in the oceans! Read these questions to the kids without letting them see the answers. Try some of the activities we've suggested, or come up with your own.

**1.** A blue whale's heart is the size of:
A. A microwave   B. A small car   C. A tuba
**Answer: B!**

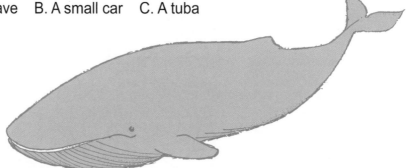

Help the kids visualize the whale's amazing size! Go to a large outdoor area. If dirt or gravel, bring along a yardstick or sticks for "drawing"; if pavement, bring chalk. Have them walk off about 100 feet, marking the length with their stick or chalk. (That's about 80 good strides for Grandma. The average woman's stride is 2.2 feet). That long mark is the bottom of the whale! Now help them complete the outline of the rest of the whales form. In the heart area, draw in the shape of the car, approximate 13 1/2 feet long. Then they can add whatever imaginative features they want such as fins and rows of "baleen". (Nope, these whales don't have teeth). Would you want to meet up with this giant creature?!

**2.** An electric eel can produce enough energy to power:
A. A desktop computer   B. A department store   C. 10 light bulbs
**Answer: C!**

Electric eels use their electricity to fend off predators as well as to stun their prey. They also can't see what they are shocking because they are mostly blind. Using radar like senses helps them find their food.

**3.** An octopus's blood is:
   A. Red    B. Green    C. Blue
   **Answer: C!**

**Odd fact:** Octopuses don't have tentacles, they are called arms!

**4.** The loudest animal sound on the planet is made by:
   A. A blue whale    B. A dolphin    C. An orca
   **Answer: A!**

The blue whale makes a sound of 188 decibels, louder than a jet which makes a sound reaching 120 decibels. Underwater, the whales sound can travel 500 miles away. Who does your grandchild know that lives 500 miles away? Ask that they imagine being able to have a conversation, without phones! Yes, grandchild Luca in Denver can hear Cousin Luisa—in Wichita!

**5.** Turtles live on every continent except:
   A. Antarctica    B. Australia    C. Europe
   **Answer: A!**

Sea turtles will migrate thousands of miles over their lifetimes. Sometimes traveling over 10,000 miles a year to find food and lay eggs. Turtles have a special tool to navigate these epic voyages— an internal GPS using the earth's magnetic field.

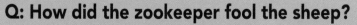

**Q: How did the zookeeper fool the sheep?**
A: She pulled the wool over their eyes!

**6.** The only animal in which males give birth and care for the young is
   A. A pufferfish   B. An octopus   C. A seahorse
   **Answer: C!**

The male seahorse carries the eggs in his pouch until they hatch, then releases fully formed, miniature seahorses into the water. As little as 5 or as many as 1,500 young can be born.

**7.** The world's smallest sea creature is smaller than a postage stamp! It is
   A. A clownfish   B. A seahorse   C. A sea star
   **Answer: B!**
   Imagine a teensy animal fitting on a postage stamp! Draw postage stamp size squares, or copy and cut out the one shown here. With fine line markers or pencils, have kids create their own imaginative, diminutive creatures.

**8.** Some jellyfish tentacles stretch more than
   A. 100 feet   B. 20 feet   C. 2 miles
   **Answer: A!**

**9.** Manatees are related to
   A. Elephants   B. Lions   C. Hippopotamuses
   **Answer: A!**
   The manatee is also called a "sea cow" as it's known for its large, slow, lolling, peaceful, plant-eating nature.

### USE YOUR SENSE!
   Create an area with different textures for children to touch (oh, THAT sense!) Around a room, place a sheet of sandpaper, a swatch of fuzzy fabric, a piece of leather, etc. Blindfold the grandkids and invite them to explore your "wildlife center". Guide them to each "exhibit" to touch the texture and imagine what animal they might be meeting.

# CHAPTER 7: THE GREAT OUTDOORS

*Wildlife, seeds, trees and tracks...Get out there with the kids and explore the wondrous world of nature!*

## TAKE A HIKE!

Next time you are out and about in the wild, be on the lookout for unusual signs and events. For example:

Did you know that the leaves on a tree turn upside-down before a storm? That's because the shifting winds blow the leaves upward.

A mountain mahogany seedling has a corkscrew shape on one end. Why? So the seedling can penetrate into the ground.

Afraid you'll get lost in the woods? Just check the trees for moss. In the northern hemisphere, moss tends to grow only on the north side of trees. In the southern hemisphere, it grows on the south side. Why? These sides are away from direct sun and provide the cooler environment moss likes best.

A forest fire is a very frightening concept, but let the kids know fierce fires can actually benefit some plants. The jack pine seals its seeds inside cones. Nothing can penetrate the hard, sticky sap that seals these cones—except fire. The heat from a blaze melts the sap and frees the seeds. Without fire, the jack pine could not survive. If you ever see an area of regrowth after a fire, you can show the kids the bright green plants returning, with new hope.

Animal homes can be anywhere! Look up into the trees for bird, squirrel, or wasp nests. Chipmunks and mice can nest under logs, in gaps between rocks, and even under piles of leaves.

# V'S IN THE TREES!

If you ask a young child to draw a tree, it will typically be a simple shape like this, sort of like a lolly pop just standing on top of the ground:

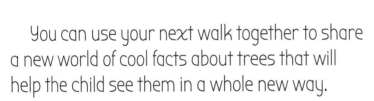

You can use your next walk together to share a new world of cool facts about trees that will help the child see them in a whole new way.

Start with the roots. Point out how the roots go into the earth, and that underneath the ground where we cannot see, the roots are branching out, possibly as far as twenty feet in some cases. Walk that off and have them to imagine the hidden roots stretching out all that way! Often the expanse of the roots mirrors the top of the tree. Explain that the tree, in order to grow, needs water and nutrients, and the roots are branching out to search for those things. Next, the nutrients and water will be delivered into the trunk, and from there carried into the branches and leaves of the tree. Look at each part of the tree as it grows and notice how the tree limbs literally branch off into a V shape. There are thicker branches on the lower part, but each branch grows out into another V...and each of those branches into another V...and each of those...Well, you get the idea, the branches get narrower and narrow, smaller and smaller all the way to the top.

Now help your child see how many times they can keep branching out into more and more v's in their new drawing of a more realistic, living tree.

# COLLECTING NATURE

Lay a white sheet on the ground in the yard or park. Give it time, then take a look at what has landed on your sheet. You'll probably see many different insects. Can you identify them all? What about pollen or bits of plants blown there by the wind? Make a chart or draw pictures of what you discover.

**Q: How far can a dog run into the woods?**
A: The dog can run into the woods only halfway –
if it runs any farther it will be running out of the woods!

# PAPIER-MÂCHÉ BUGS

Maybe you have spent time together outdoors and ended up spotting some interesting looking insects. Here is a way to bring your grandkid's imagination to bold measures. Create supersized wild and whimsical bugs! Whatever the ages, kids can take part in all the preparations. For the glue, you can either use a pre-made mix found in hobby stores or a simple mixture of flour and water, which the kids can stir up till it's a nice glue-like texture.

You will need:

- A bowl of glue mixture, whatever you choose from the options above

- 1" wide strips of newspaper, plus extra newspaper for forming shapes

- Bendable wire, such as a thin metal clothes hanger

- Masking tape

- Add-ons to fuel the imagination: feathers, ping pong balls, foam, paint, pipe cleaners, straws...you get the idea

You might encourage kids to make sketches of their wild bugs to choose from. Spread a covering to protect your work surface. Wad, roll and twist newspaper to form the shapes to make the bug. Tape together with masking tape. Build up areas as needed and wrap tape round and round. Other forms might be used, such as 1/2 ping pong balls or foam. If you have ideas for wings or legs that require wire, wrap the wire around the form and bend and shape as needed. When the basic shape is formed, you will cover it with the papier mâché. Lay a paper strip in the glue. Have the child run their fingers down the strip to remove excess glue back into the bowl. (It's sooo tempting to want to plunk down a very glue-laden strip). Cover well—but keep in mind the more layers, the longer the drying time. And now you have to wait. Go to the zoo, have a camp out, take a walk... this might take a day or two. It's fun to see the hardened form, then it's easier to imagine the possibilities. Now let them go to town bringing the features out! Start by painting with kid-safe paints or markers. Let dry. Now glue on all kinds of fun features, eye balls, fuzzy brows, antennae, spots... the only thing that might have even more creative bugs is Nature herself!

# ANIMAL TRACK MATCH-UP

Image you are out on the trail and come upon these animal tracks. Can you name the animal that made them? For a hint, think about the size, shape and ways those feet might be used. For more help, turn to the next pages where the animals are pictured and see if you can match them up.

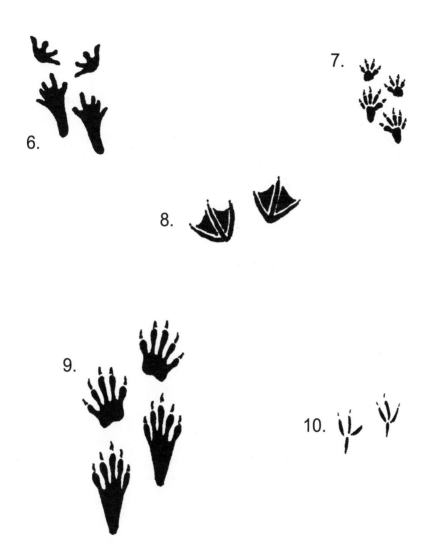

6.

7.

8.

9.

10.

## TINY FOOTPRINTS, BIG DISCOVERY!

In 2018, hikers found what experts believe are the oldest tracks ever to be discovered in the Grand Canyon. The small reptilian-like prints found inside a fallen rock showed a unique side-stepping diagonal pattern.

A. Bear—I have strong and powerful feet, made for climbing, swimming, running and walking—sometimes on just two feet!

B. Mouse—My feet are so tiny it may be hard to see my tracks.

C. Duck—My two feet are designed to walk on land and swim in the pond.

D. Toad—You might see me making little hops—my feet help with that.

E. Rabbit—My back feet are very long compared to my front. They help me run and jump fast to get away from animals that would like to make me their dinner.

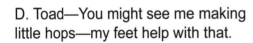

F. Skunk—On each foot I have five "toes"—but my feet are not my best defense, as anyone who has threatened me "nose."

G. Deer—I don't have claws or paws—because my feet are hooves!

H. Coyote—I have four claws on each foot. Sometimes people think my tracks look like those of their dog.

I. Crow—My feet help me perch on a branch way up high.

J. Raccoon—My feet are kind of like human hands. I wash and hold my food with them.

# CAST ANIMAL TRACKS

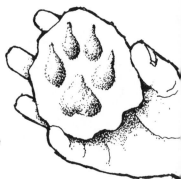

Making a cast of an animal track is a great way to preserve it. The kids will think it is so cool to show their friends the tracks that they captured. Have these supplies on hand, then look for tracks, especially in the mud after rain.

You will need:
• 5-lb. bag of plaster of Paris (available at craft or hardware stores)
• Water
• Snack-size plastic bags
• Plastic containers to mix the plaster
• Old measuring cup
• Wooden paint-stirring sticks or plastic spoons
• Old party hats with the tops cut off
• Wax paper
• Plastic containers to store your finished molds

[NOTE: It's best to use old spoon, cups, and containers for this activity, as you will not be able to wash the plaster off when you're done.]

**Step 1:** Before you go outside, pour the dry plaster of Paris into the sandwich bags, one cup per bag.

**Step 2:** Venture out to a muddy area and find some tracks that you want to mold. You can bring a pocket-sized nature guide on your trip to help you identify tracks.

**Step 3:** Once you have found a track, check the water-to-plaster ratio on the bag of plaster. Then add the correct amount water to a plastic container. Slowly pour in the right amount of plaster.

**Step 4:** Stir with the wooden sticks or spoons until the mixture is like pancake batter, with no lumps or bubbles. You have about 15 minutes to work before the plaster gets too hard to pour.

**Step 5:** Place a party hat around the track to hold in the plaster.

**Step 6:** Carefully pour the plaster mixture into the track. You will have better results if you pour from the side and let the mixture seep into the track instead of pouring straight down.

**Step 7:** Let the plaster harden. This takes at least 30 minutes. Resist the urge to touch or poke the plaster while it dries!

**Step 8:** Dig out the cast, being very careful not to break or chip it. The plaster may still be a little sticky.

**Step 9:** Wrap the cast in wax paper and place it in a clean container.

**Step 10:** Let the casts dry outside for another 24 hours. Then have fun showing off your tracks to family and friends!

# FOLLOW THOSE TRACKS!

Look for animal tracks! This activity works best on a muddy or snowy day. Can you identify each animal by its track? Look at the size and shape of the track. Can you see toes and claws? What is the pattern of the footsteps? Where are they going? Take pictures or make a drawing to remember what you saw. When you get home, do some research to find out what animal made those tracks!

# BEWARE OF PLANT!

You know that many animals are carnivores—they eat other animals. But did you know that there are also carnivorous plants? Carnivorous plants usually grow in soil that does not have a lot of nutrients. That means they can't get the nutrition they need just from the soil. So what's a hungry plant to do? Go hunting for meat—specifically, insects!

How can a plant hunt if it is rooted to the ground? Deadly leaves do the job. A Venus flytrap's leaves are covered with sensitive hairs. When an insect crawls on those hairs, the leaves snap shut, trapping the poor bug inside. The leaves stay shut while digestive juices do their work.

Other carnivorous plants use the shape of their leaves to trap their prey. The pitcher plant has long, flared leaves that look like a container for water. If an insect falls inside the leaves, it ends up in a pool of digestive juices.

There are many other types of carnivorous plants. What other ones can you find?

# PAINT A ROCK!

While you are out on your walk, have the grandkids look for small flat, smooth rocks. When you're back home, have them remember things they saw on the walk and choose a rock shape on which to paint it. Use permanent marker or acrylic paint. Place these fun rocks in a garden, or put them in other places to surprise and delight those who discover them.

# IT'S AN OPTICAL ILLUSION!

There is more than meets the eye in this flower garden. How many faces can you find?

# THE GREAT OUTDOORS

Carefully chart your path to reach the stream and try to use the least amount of footprints to get through the maze?

**FUN FACT:**
Did you know to walk a mile you will make 2000 footprints to get from the beginning to the end.

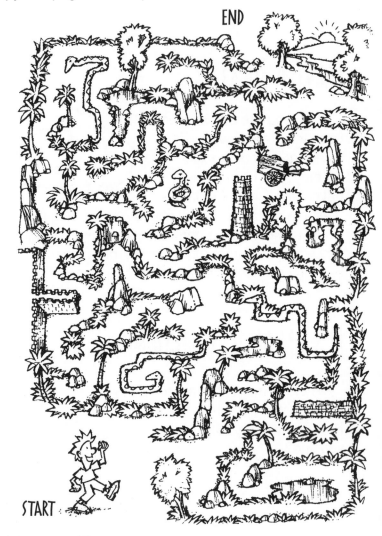

END

START

# ANIMAL TRACKS TRUE OR FALSE

Circle the correct answer.

1. **T F** Polar bears have wide front paws with webbed toes that help them swim.

2. **T F** Animals have fingerprints.

3. **T F** Birds have nails.

4. **T F** A fish can leave footprints like other animals.

5. **T F** Caterpillars have 24 eyes.

86

# CHAPTER 8: RIDDLES AND BRAIN TEASERS

*Keep your friends and family guessing—and laughing—
with these clever questions!*

## HA HA HA HA!

**Q:** Sally's mother had three daughters. Two are named April and May. What is the name of the third daughter?

**A:** Sally.

**Q:** What is the four mistake in this sentance?

**A:** 1. "Is" should be "are"; 2. "mistake" should be "mistakes"; 3. "sentance" should be spelled "sentence"; 4. There are only three mistakes!

**Q:** You walk into a room with a match, a kerosene lamp, a candle, and a fireplace. Which do you light first?

**A:** The match.

**Q:** What word begins and ends with an E but only has one letter?

**A:** Envelope.

**Q:** Which letter of the alphabet has the most water?

**A:** C.

**Q:** What goes up but never goes down?

**A:** Your age.

**Q:** What starts with the letter "T," is filled with "T," and ends in "T?"

**A:** A teapot

**Q:** What gets wetter and wetter the more it dries?

**A:** A towel.

**Q:** Railroad crossing, watch out for cars. Can you spell that without any Rs?

**A:** T-H-A-T.

# HA HA HA HA!

**Q:** A boy was rushed to the hospital emergency room. The ER doctor saw the boy and said, "I cannot operate on this boy. He is my son." But the doctor was not the boy's father. How could that be?

**A:** The doctor was his mom.

**Q:** What belongs to you but other people use it more than you?

**A:** Your name.

**Q:** I have a large money box, 10 inches wide and 5 inches tall. Roughly how many coins can I place in my empty money box?

**A:** Just one, after which it will no longer be empty.

**Q:** What does this mean? I RIGHT I

**A:** Right between the eyes.

**Q:** You draw a line. Without touching it, how do you make the line longer?

**A:** You draw a shorter line next to it, and it becomes the longer line.

**Q:** Which weighs more, a pound of feathers or a pound of bricks?

**A:** Neither. They both weigh one pound.

**Q:** Two mothers and two daughters went out to eat. Everyone ate one burger, yet only three burgers were eaten in all. How is this possible?

**A:** They were a grandmother, mother, and daughter.

**Q:** How many seconds are there in a year?

**A:** 12. January 2nd, February 2nd, March 2nd, April 2nd …

**Q:** A cowboy rides into town on Friday, stays for three days, then leaves on Friday. How did he do it?

**A:** His horse's name was Friday.

**Q:** You walk across a bridge and you see a boat full of people, yet there isn't a single person on board. How is that possible?

**A:** All the people on the boat are married.

**Q:** I have keys but no doors. I have space but no rooms, I allow you to enter but you are never able to leave. What am I?

**A:** A keyboard.

**Q:** How many months have 28 days?
**A:** All 12 months.

**Q:** Name four days of the week that start with the letter "T."
**A:** Tuesday, Thursday, today, and tomorrow.

**Q:** What comes once in a minute, twice in a moment, but never in a thousand years?
**A:** The letter M.

**Q:** What goes around and around the wood, but never goes into the wood?
**A:** The bark on a tree.

**Q:** A boy fell off a 20-foot ladder but did not get hurt. Why not?
**A:** He fell off the bottom step.

**Q:** Using only addition, how do you add eight 8s and get the number 1,000?
**A:** 888 + 88 + 8 + 8 + 8 = 1000.

**Q:** How do dog catchers get paid?
**A:** By the pound.

**Q:** What never asks questions but is often answered?
**A:** A doorbell.

**Q:** The more you take, the more you leave behind. What are they?
**A:** Footprints.

**Q:** What two keys can't open any door?
**A:** A monkey and a donkey.

**Q:** What invention lets you look right through a wall?
**A:** A window.

**Q:** What five-letter word becomes shorter when you add two letters to it?
**A:** Short.

**Q:** Imagine you're in a room that is filling with water. There are no windows or doors. How do you get out?
**A:** Stop imagining.

# HA HA HA HA!

**Q:** How is Europe like a frying pan?
**A:** Because it has Greece at the bottom.

**Q:** What kind of tree can you carry in your hand?
**A:** A palm.

**Q:** What do the numbers 11, 69, and 88 all have in common?
**A:** They read the same right side up and upside down.

**Q:** How can you throw a ball as hard as you can, to only have it come back to you, even if it doesn't bounce off anything?
**A:** Throw the ball straight up in the air.

**Q:** Why are ghosts bad liars?
**A:** You can see right through them.

**Q:** What has one eye but can't see?
**A:** A needle.

**Q:** I am an odd number. Take away one letter and I become even. What number am I?
**A:** Seven (take away the "s" and it becomes "even").

**Q:** What word looks the same backwards and upside down?
**A:** SWIMS.

**Q:** What's the difference between a schoolteacher and a subway conductor?
**A:** The teacher trains the mind, while the conductor minds the train!

**Q:** What's the difference between a dog and a flea?
**A:** A dog can have fleas, but a flea can't have dogs!

**Q:** What's the difference between a jewelry store owner and a ship's captain?
**A:** The jewelry store owner sees the watches, while the ship's captain watches the seas!

**I saw Esau sitting on a seesaw. Esau, he saw me.**

How fast can you say that?

# SOLUTIONS

## PAGE 11

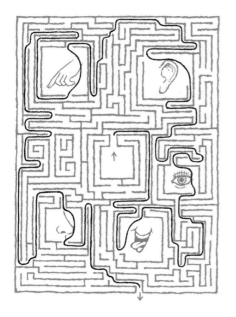

Amazing Senses True or False
1. **TRUE**—Under the right condions the human eye can see a candle light 1.6 miles away. But, if you used a pair of binoculars you could see it from 10 miles away.
2. **TRUE**—Research has shown that a chemical is released when someone is scared that can actually be smelled.
3. **TRUE**—The tongue surface features are a unique characteristic of every individual just like a fingerprint.
4. **FALSE**—Your sense of hearing depends on tiny hairs deep inside your ear. If you lose these hairs, you lose your hearing.
5. **TRUE**—The skin is the coat to the human body. It's called the epidermus and is the largest organ of the body.

## PAGE 22

Wacky Foods True or False
1. **FALSE**—Spaghetti is made with a mixture of flour, egg and water.
2. **TRUE**—Honey never goes bad. It's the only recognized food that never spoils. Over time it crystalizes and gets cloudy but all that needs to be done is to place the jar in warm water and it becomes like new.
3. **TRUE**—The pizza measured 122 feet; 8 inches in diameter; weighed 26,883 pounds; and contained 9,920 pounds of flour; 4,000 pounds of cheese; 1,763 pounds of...

## PAGE 22 CONT'D

Wacky Foods True or False
3. ...1,763 pounds of mushrooms; 1,984 pounds of tomato puree; and 1,984 pounds of chopped tomatoes. WOW!
4. **TRUE**—There are over 350 shapes of pasta all around the world and 4 times as many names for them!
5. **TRUE**—Funny that chickens have earlobes...but they do. Chickens with white earlobes usually lay white eggs, while a dard red or brown earlobed chicken will lay brown eggs.

## PAGE 33

Matchstick Math: Move the bottom matchstick to the right to make the 2 a number 3.

## PAGE 38

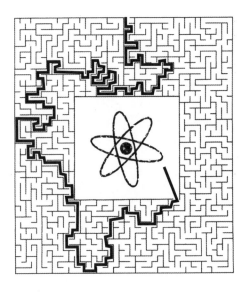

## PAGE 42

One windy day.
Electric trains don't have smoke.

Odd and Strange True or False
1. **TRUE**—The phenomenon that hot water may freeze faster than cold is often called the Mpemba effect. This phenomenon has been known for centuries by not popularized until 1969 by a high school student named Mpemba.
2. **FALSE**—The truth is that we really don't know but experts think it's between 5,000 to 60,000 thoughts.
3. **TRUE**— Even though the numbers vary everyday the average seems to be around 41 new species are discovered each day by scientists.
4. **FALSE**—The moon is similar to Earth in its composition but no one really knows yet. Sadly the astronauts found no cheese on the moon.
5. **TRUE**— The days have been getting longer and longer since the dinosur age and most think that millions of years ago the day was only 23 hours.

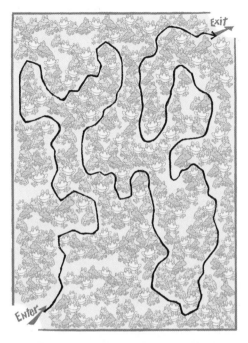

Stormy and Wild True or False
1. **FALSE**—Although it's true for most people, there are some that can sneeze repeatedly without blinking once.
2. **TRUE**— The Golden poison frog also know as the Dart frog is possibly the most poisonous animal on the planet. They are brightly colored, and in nature, bright colors are often a warning sign to stay away.
3. **TRUE**— Although this seems odd, it's true. A record breaking 15 inch snowflake fell in Montana, 1887.
4. **TRUE**— 97% of the Earth's water is salt water that humans can't drink. 2% is frozen, and so that leaves 1% of the Earth's water that is easy to access and safe to drink.
5. **TRUE**— While warm weather causes tires to over inflate, cold weather does the opposite and causes tires to lose pressure.

Magically True or False
1. **TRUE**— The world's fastest magician (Dr. Eldoonie) once performed 255 effects in two minutes.
2. **TRUE**— When the largest playing card company in the country turns on its printing presses they print 10 decks of cards every second.
3. **FALSE**—There are no colleges that offer a degree in magic. There are however, a number of places that you can study magic to learn new skills and become a professional.

## PAGE 51 CONT'D

4. **FALSE**—While not something that can be proved, many magicians wear the moustache to make them look more magical.
5. **FALSE**—While not all hats are sold with a rabbit, the rabbit and hat trick has been around since 1814.

## PAGE 60

Find the hidden cat.

## PAGE 61

Monkey Time

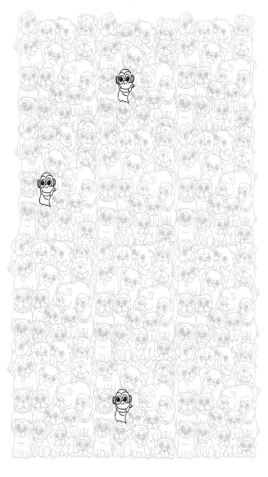

**PAGE 69**

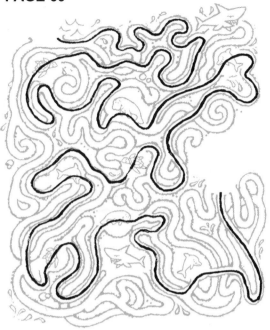

Deep Blue True or False
1. **TRUE**— Well kind of. Some believe that 94% of all life on earth lives in the ocean. But it's hard to say because we have only explored about 5% of the ocean so far.
2. **TRUE**— Jellyfish are more dangerous than sharks.There is a species (IRUKANDJI JELLYFISH) that is only 1/4 of an inch long but is 100 times more poisonous than a king cobra snake.
3. **FALSE**—Seahorse wrap their tail to coral and rest...but they do sleep upright, with their eyes open.
4. **TRUE**— 12 people have walked on the moon's surface, but only 3 have ever been to the bottom of the ocean.
5. **TRUE**— There are waterfalls, lakes, and rivers in the ocean! They are formed by differences in the water salt content and act just like they do above the surface.

**PAGE 78-81**

Animal Track Match Up
ANSWERS:
A5; B7; C8; D6;
E3; F2; G4; H1; I10; J9

**PAGE 85**

Hidden Faces

Animal Tracks True or False
1. **TRUE**— Polar bears have wide front paws with webbed toes that help them swim. They use the front paws to paddle and the rear feet to steer.
2. **TRUE**— Some animals have fingerprints like Gorillas and Koalas that are similar to human fingerprints. However, many have ridges that are like fingerprints that help them grip and climb.
3. **TRUE**— Birds do have nails or claws.They don't look like those of humans but play a vital role in gathering food and fetching prey.
4. **TRUE**— Some fish can leave footprints like other animals. Mudskippers and lungfish can breath air and move across land between bodies of water leaving behind a footprint.
5. **FALSE**—But caterpillars do have 12 eyes. They have six on each side of their head. They can't see images, only shades of light and dark but are very sensitive.

## RIDDLE:
## WHAT CAN YOU ALWAYS FIND AT GRANDMA'S HOUSE?

### ANSWER:
## ARMS FILLED WITH HUGS, HEARTS FILLED WITH LOVE,
## JARS FILLED WITH COOKIES, AND DAYS FILLED WITH COOL FUN!